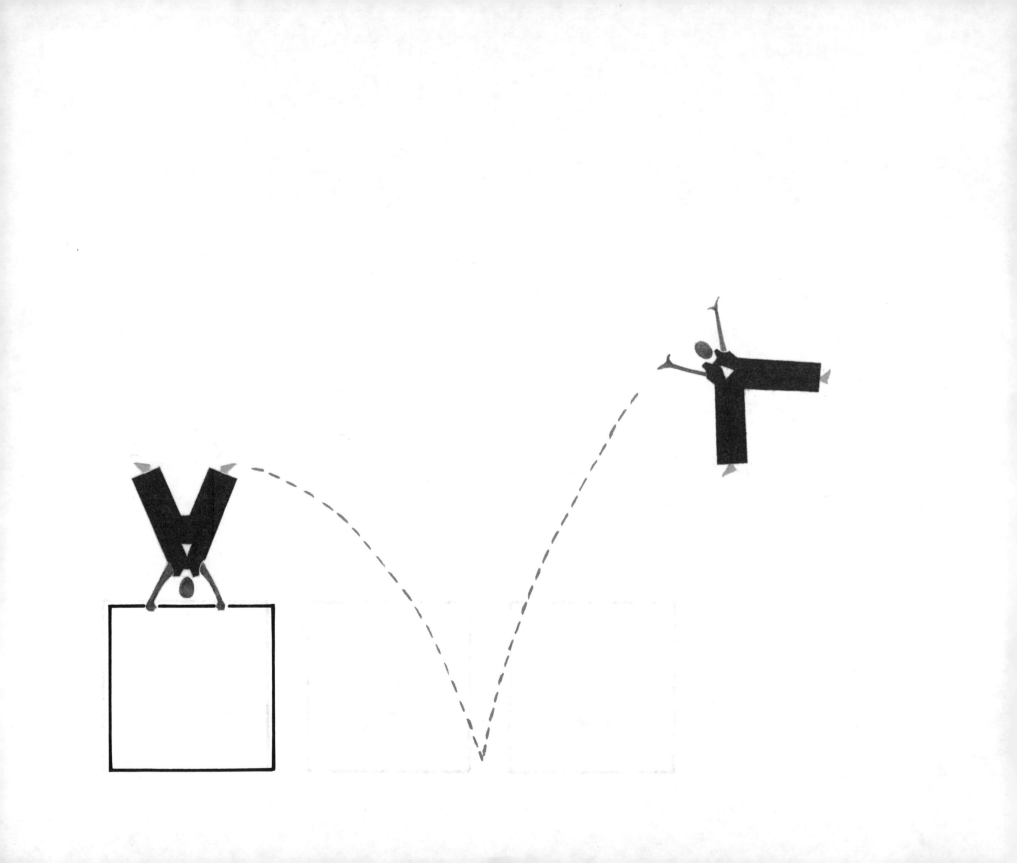

ALPHABATICS

Suse MacDonald

A TRUMPET CLUB SPECIAL EDITION

Aa

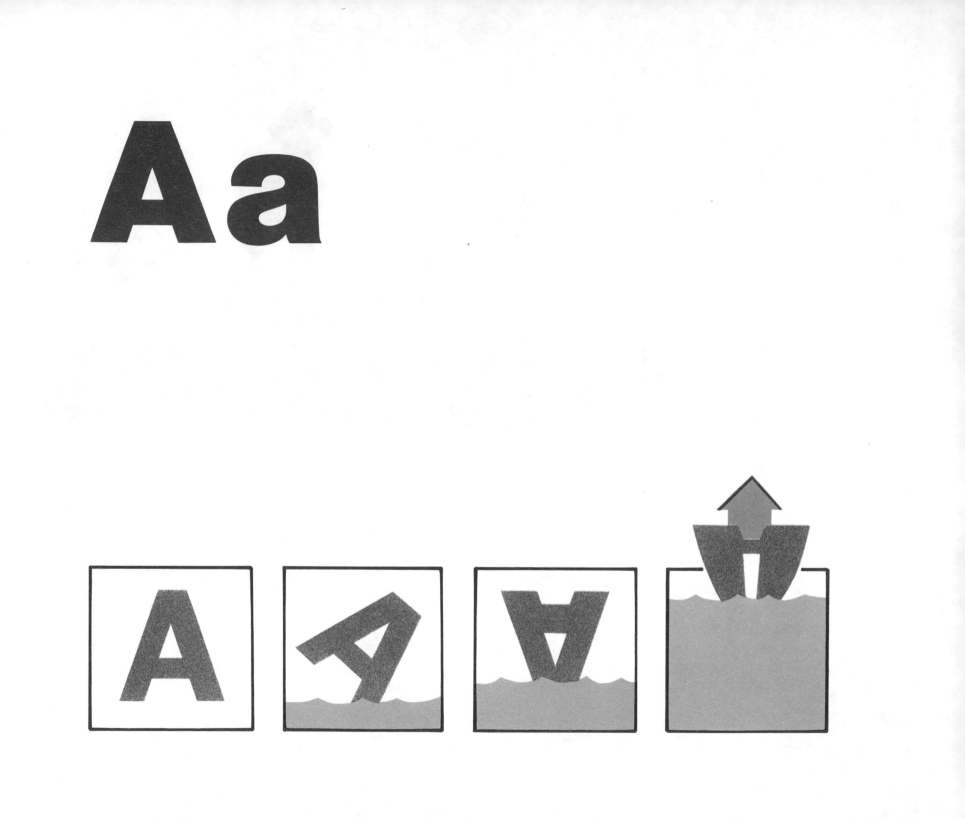

Ark

balloon

Cc

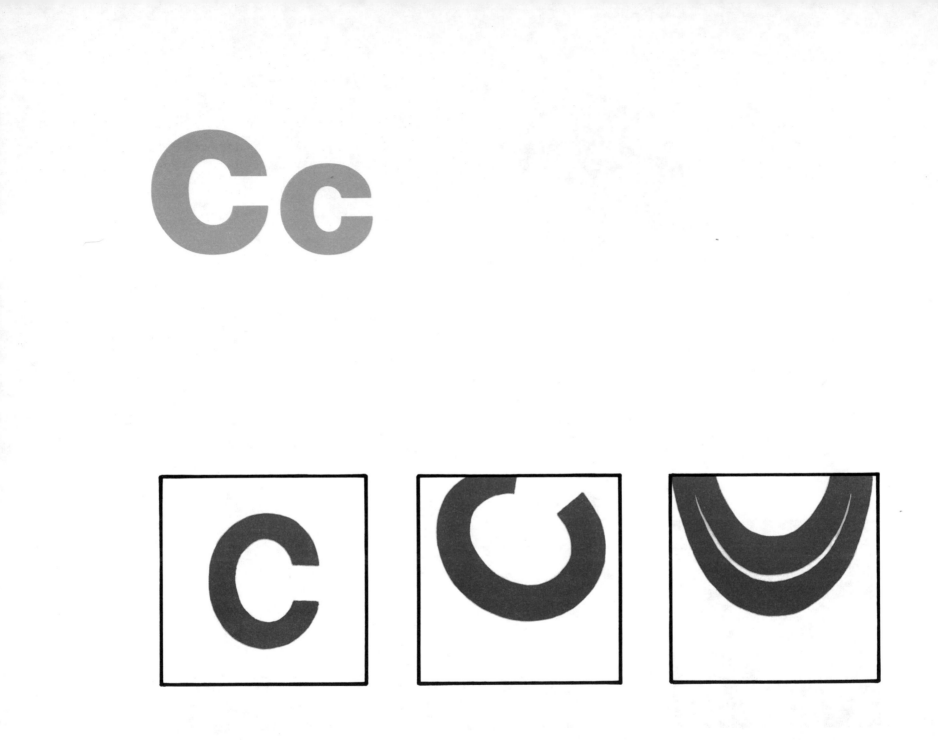

Clown

Dd

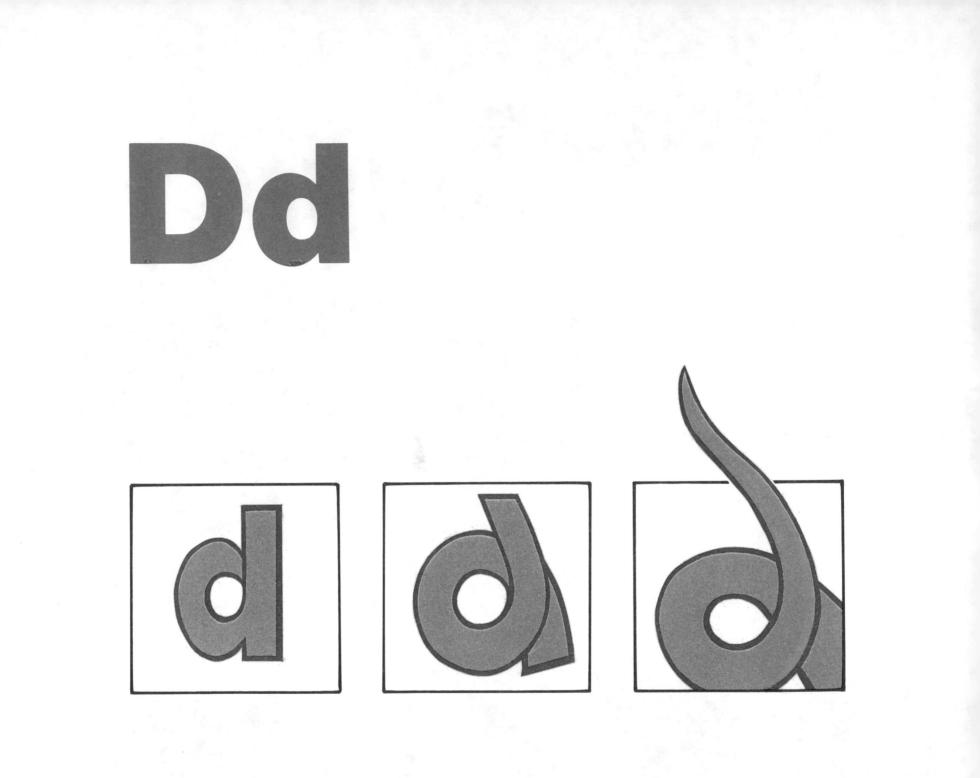

dragon

Elephant

Fish

Giraffe

house

insect

jack-
in-the-box

Kite

Ll

Lion

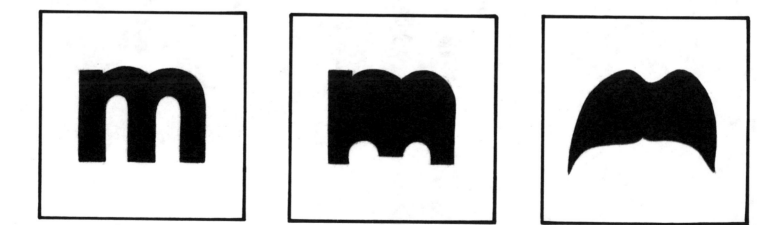

mustache

nest

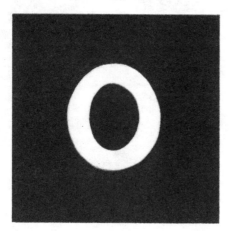  

owl

Plane

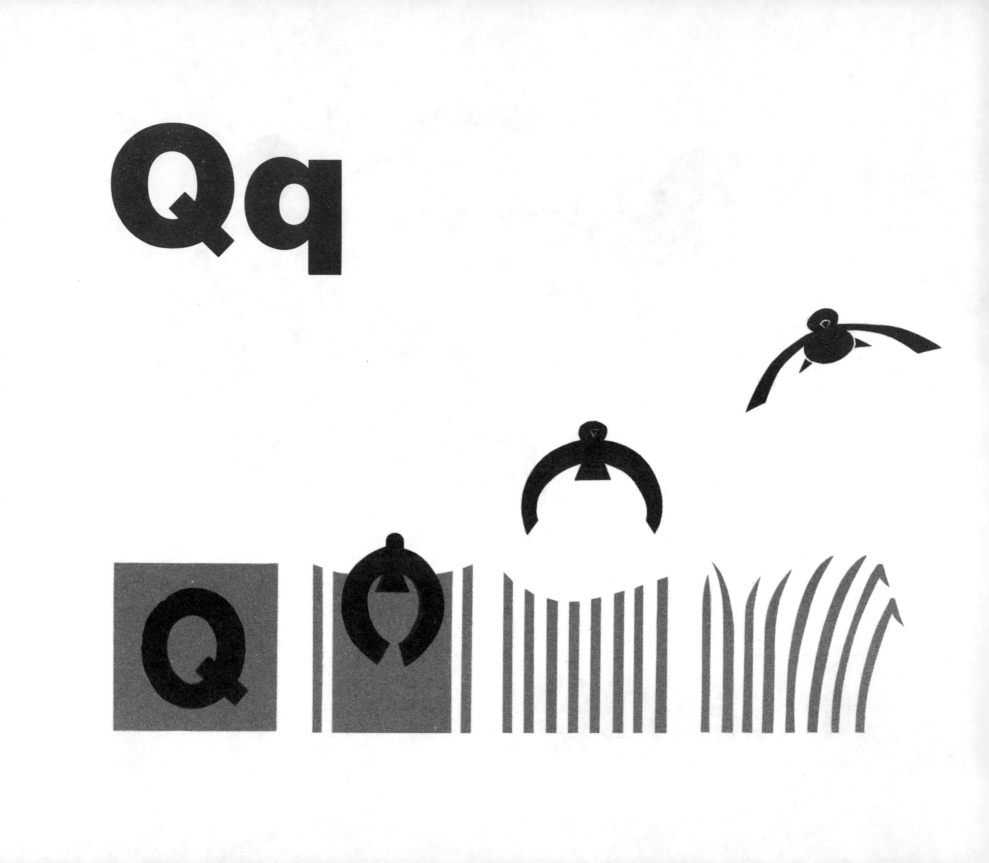

Quail

rooster

Ss

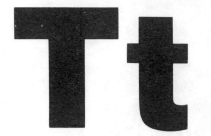

Tree

umbrella

Vegetables

Whale

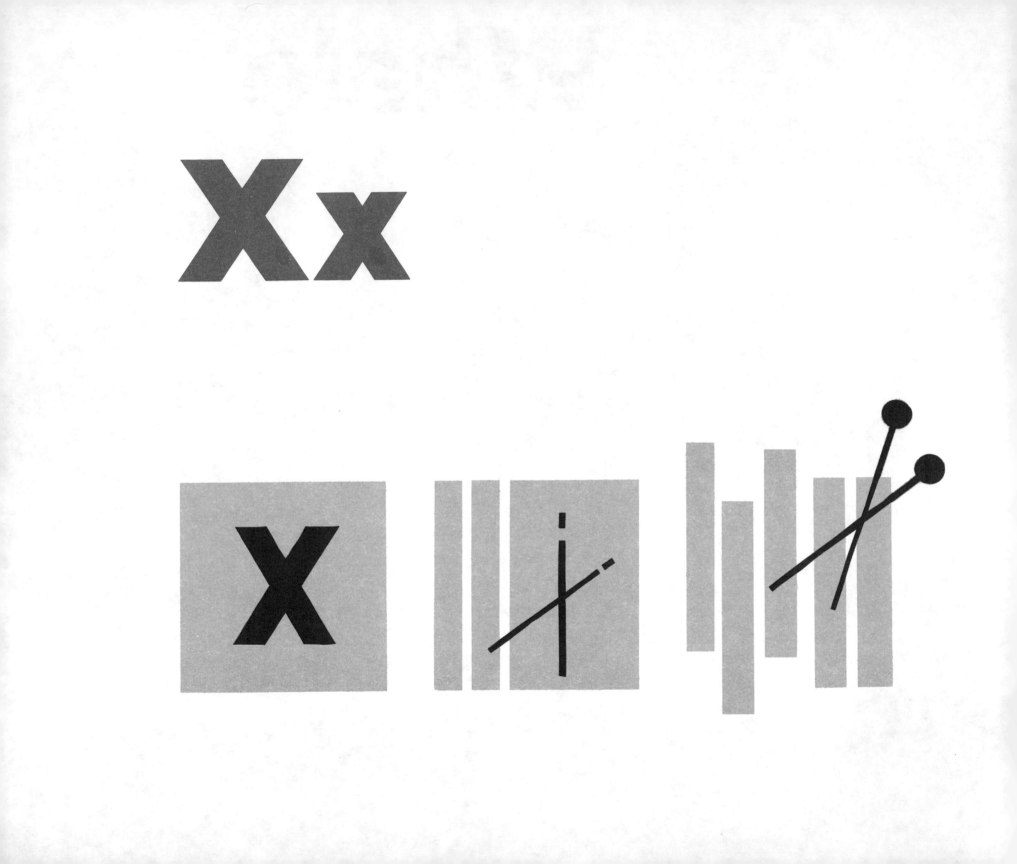

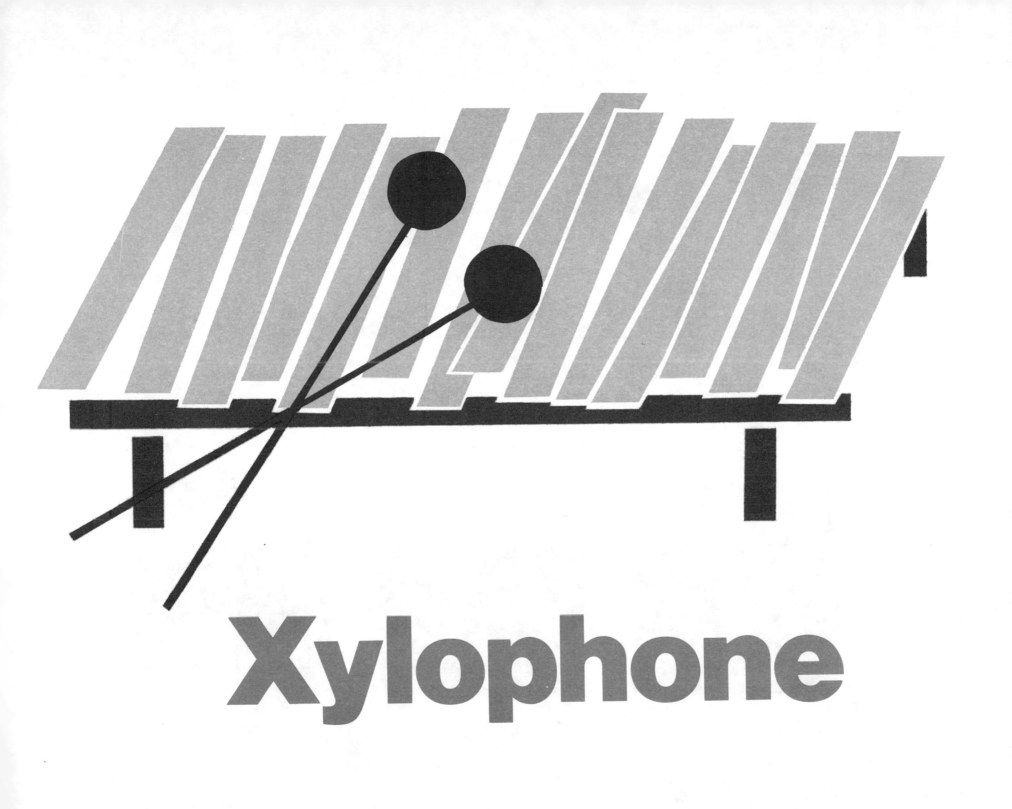

Xylophone

Yy

Yak

Zebra

For Stuart, with special thanks to Susan and Deborah

Published by The Trumpet Club, 666 Fifth Avenue, New York, New York 10103

ISBN: 0-440-84473-8

This edition published by arrangement with Bradbury Press, an affiliate of Macmillan Publishing Company
Printed in the United States of America   October 1991
10 9 8 7 6 5 4 3 2 1
UPC